Theory Paper Grade 1 2019 A

Duration 1½ hours

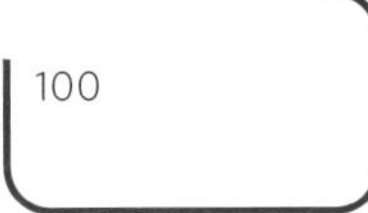

Candidates should answer ALL questions.
Write your answers on this paper – no others will be accepted.
Answers must be written clearly and neatly – otherwise marks may be lost.

1 (a) Add the time signature to each of these three melodies.

(b) Add the missing bar-lines to this melody. The first bar-line is given.

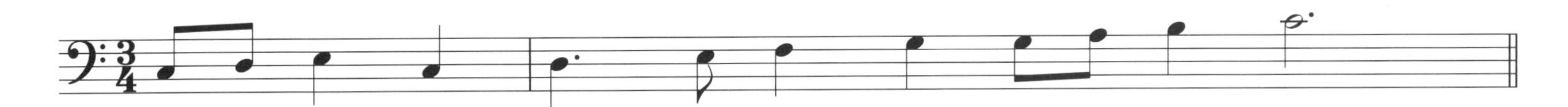

2 Name the major keys shown by these key signatures. The first answer is given.

10

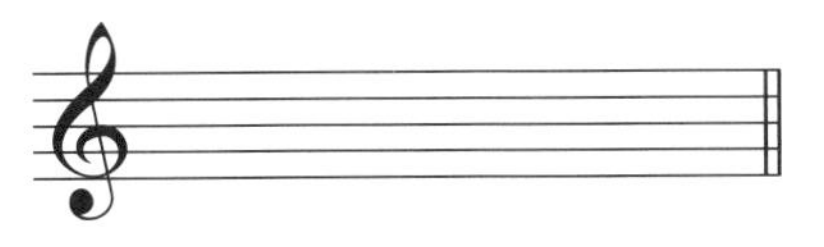

C major

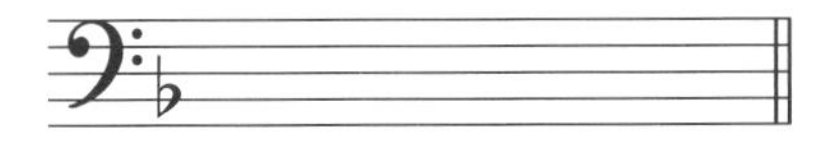

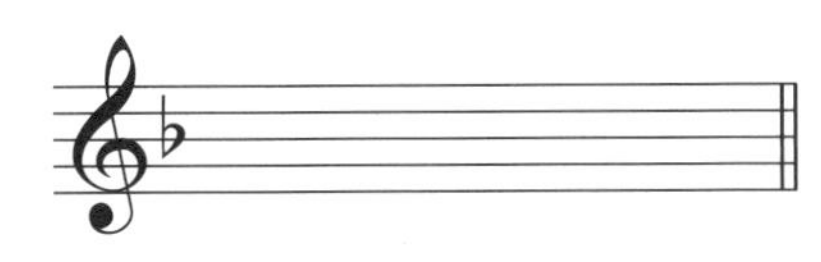

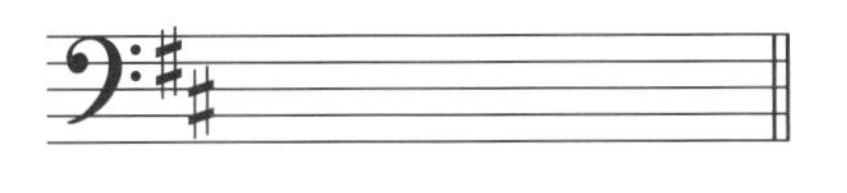

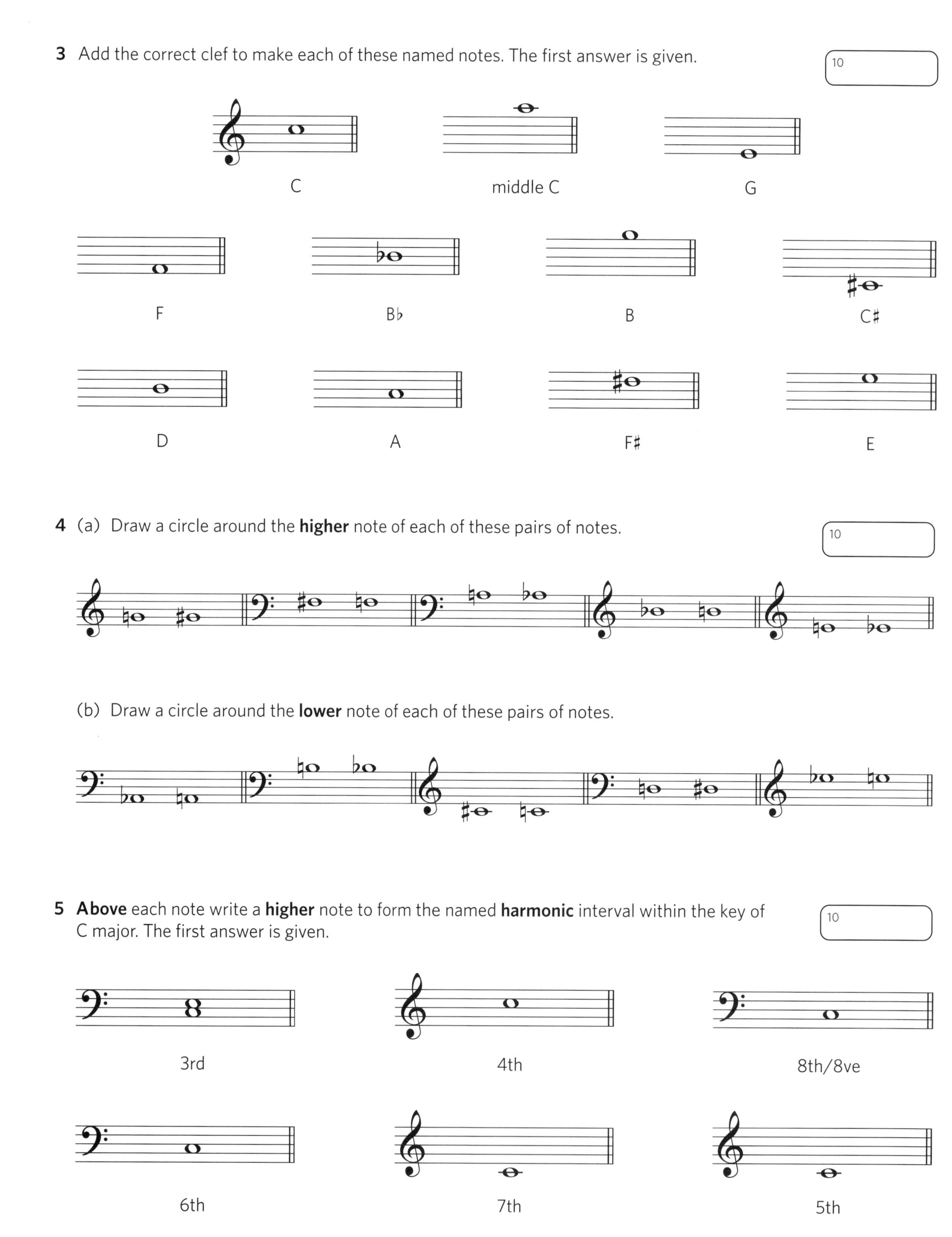
3 Add the correct clef to make each of these named notes. The first answer is given.
10
C
middle C
G
F
B♭
B
C♯
D
A
F♯
E
4 (a) Draw a circle around the higher note of each of these pairs of notes.
10
(b) Draw a circle around the lower note of each of these pairs of notes.
5 Above each note write a higher note to form the named harmonic interval within the key of C major. The first answer is given.
10
3rd
4th
8th/8ve
6th
7th
5th

Grade
1

Music Theory Practice Papers 2019

ABRSM Grade 1

Music Theory Practice Papers 2019

ABRSM's *Music Theory Practice Papers 2019* are based on the 2019 Music Theory exam papers. The questions are the same as those used in recent exams.

Find out more about our Music Theory exams at **www.abrsm.org/theory**.

Published by ABRSM (Publishing) Ltd, a wholly owned subsidiary of ABRSM
Cover by Kate Benjamin & Andy Potts
Printed in England by Halstan & Co. Ltd, Amersham, Bucks., on materials from sustainable sources

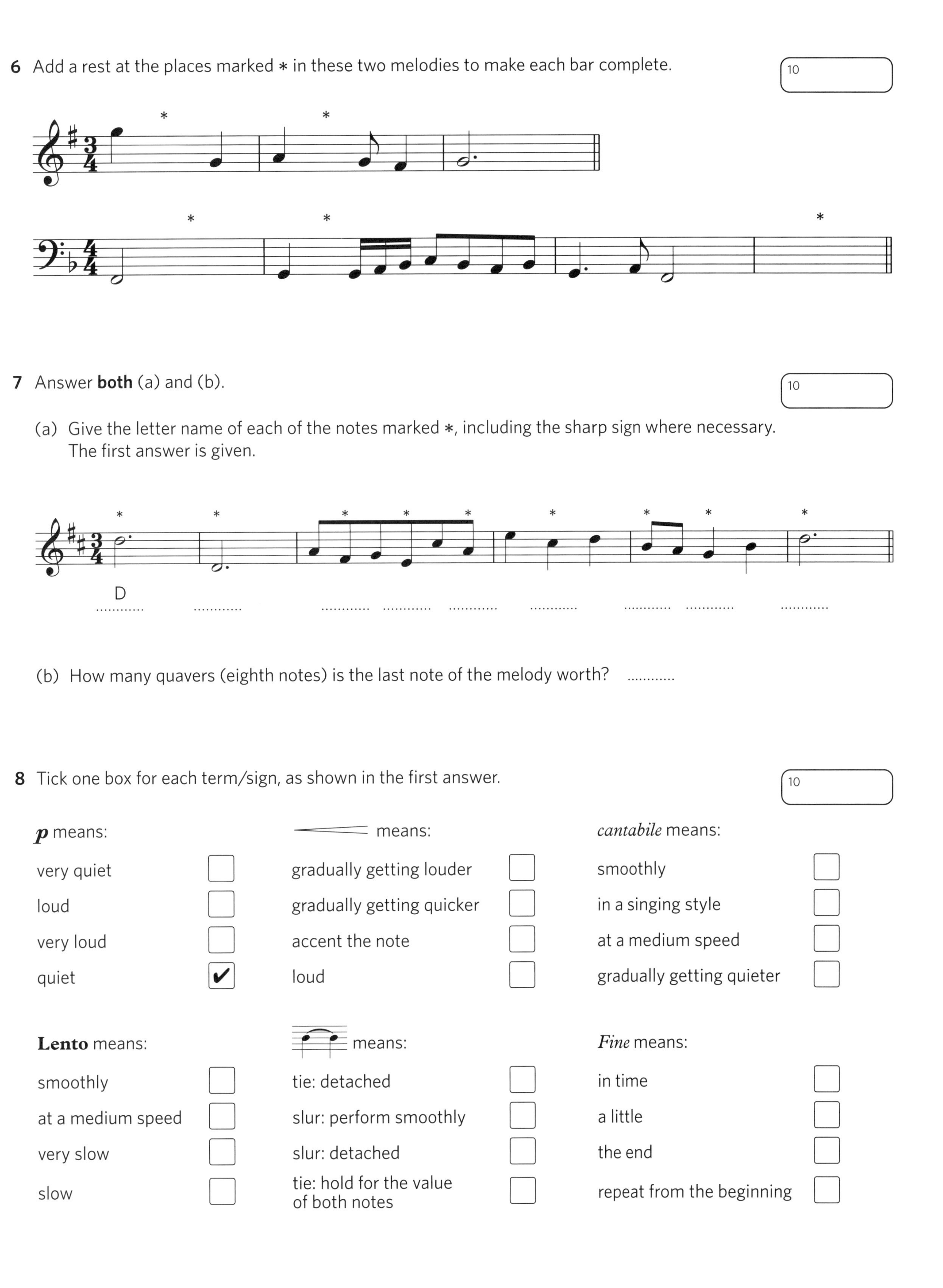
6 Add a rest at the places marked * in these two melodies to make each bar complete.
10
7 Answer both (a) and (b).
10
(a) Give the letter name of each of the notes marked *, including the sharp sign where necessary. The first answer is given.
D
(b) How many quavers (eighth notes) is the last note of the melody worth?
8 Tick one box for each term/sign, as shown in the first answer.
10
p means:
very quiet
loud
very loud
quiet
means:
gradually getting louder
gradually getting quicker
accent the note
loud
cantabile means:
smoothly
in a singing style
at a medium speed
gradually getting quieter
Lento means:
smoothly
at a medium speed
very slow
slow
means:
tie: detached
slur: perform smoothly
slur: detached
tie: hold for the value of both notes
Fine means:
in time
a little
the end
repeat from the beginning

9 Look at this melody and then answer the questions below.

Write your answer to question (b) on the stave below.

(a) (i) How many bars contain a dotted crotchet (dotted quarter note)? ....

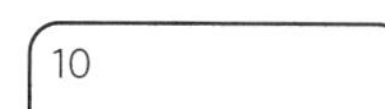

(ii) Give the time name (e.g. crotchet or quarter note) of the **longest** note in the melody. ....

(iii) Give the letter name of the **lowest** note in the melody. ....

(iv) Complete this sentence:

Bar 2 has the same notes and rhythm as bar ....

(v) Underline one of the following words that describes how bar 3 should be played.

legato (smoothly) or *staccato* (detached)

(b) Copy out the music from the start of bar 5 to the end of bar 8, exactly as it is written above. Don't forget the clef, key signature, dynamics and all other details. Write the music on the blank stave above question (a).

10

Theory Paper Grade 1 2019 B

Duration 1½ hours

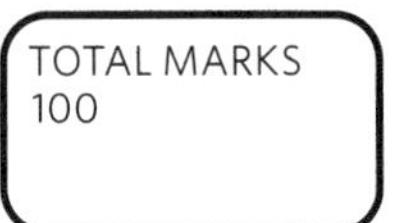

Candidates should answer ALL questions.
Write your answers on this paper – no others will be accepted.
Answers must be written clearly and neatly – otherwise marks may be lost.

1 Add the missing bar-lines to these two melodies. The first bar-line is given in each.

2 Answer **both** (a) and (b).

(a) Add the correct clef to each of these tonic triads.

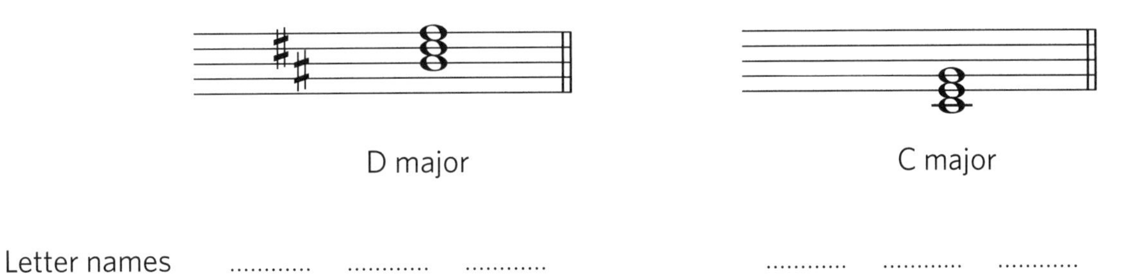

(b) Under each triad write the letter name of each note, including the sharp sign where necessary.

3 Using semibreves (whole notes), write one octave of the scales named below.
Do **not** use key signatures, but remember to add any necessary accidentals.

10

G major, ascending

F major, descending

4 Give the number (e.g. 2nd, 3rd) of each of these melodic intervals, as shown in the first answer.
The key is D major.

10

6th
....

....

....

....

....

....

5 Next to each note write a rest that has the same time value. The first answer is given.

10

6 Answer **both** (a) and (b).

10

(a) Name the degree of the scale (e.g. 2nd, 3rd) of each of the notes marked ∗, as shown in the first answer. The key is G major.

3rd ....

(b) Give the time name (e.g. crotchet or quarter note) of the **longest** note in the melody. ....

7 Write the time values ♪ ♩. 𝅗𝅥 ♩ 𝅘𝅥𝅯 𝅝 in the correct order, from the **longest** to the **shortest**. The first answer is given.

10

𝅝 ....

8 Tick one box for each term, as shown in the first answer.

10

poco means:

- detached ☐
- in time ☐
- a little ☑
- the end ☐

legato means:

- smoothly ☐
- very quiet ☐
- gradually getting slower ☐
- detached ☐

pp means:

- very loud ☐
- moderately loud ☐
- moderately quiet ☐
- very quiet ☐

ritenuto means:

- gradually getting quicker ☐
- slow ☐
- held back ☐
- gradually getting slower ☐

diminuendo means:

- gradually getting quieter ☐
- gradually getting louder ☐
- gradually getting quicker ☐
- quiet ☐

Allegro means:

- fairly quick ☐
- quick ☐
- at a medium speed ☐
- slow ☐

9 Look at this melody and then answer the questions below.

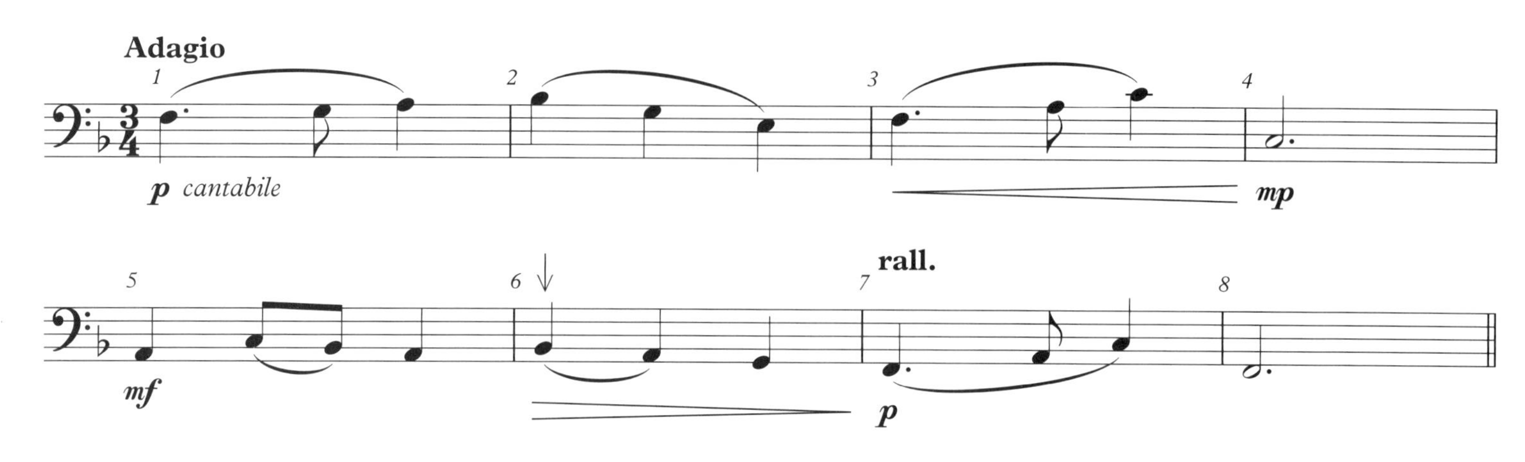

Write your answer to question (b) on the stave below.

(a) (i) Give the number of a bar that contains **all** the notes of the tonic triad of F major. Bar ....

10

(ii) How many times does the rhythm ♩. ♪ ♩ occur? ....

(iii) Give the letter name of the first note in bar 6 (marked ↓). ....

(iv) Answer TRUE or FALSE to these sentences:

The melody gets gradually quicker in bar 7. ....

$\frac{3}{4}$ means three crotchet (quarter-note) beats in a minute. ....

(b) Copy out the music from the start of bar 1 to the end of bar 4, exactly as it is written above. Don't forget the clef, key signature, time signature, tempo marking, dynamics and all other details. Write the music on the blank stave above question (a).

10

Theory Paper Grade 1 2019 C

Duration 1½ hours

TOTAL MARKS
100

Candidates should answer ALL questions.
Write your answers on this paper – no others will be accepted.
Answers must be written clearly and neatly – otherwise marks may be lost.

1 (a) Add the time signature to each of these three melodies.

(b) Add the missing bar-lines to this melody. The first bar-line is given.

2 Write the dynamics ***f*** ***mp*** ***ff*** ***pp*** ***p*** ***mf*** in the correct order, from the **loudest** to the **quietest**. The first answer is given.

10

ff ....

3 Answer **both** (a) and (b).

10

(a) Name the degree of the scale (e.g. 2nd, 3rd) of each of the notes marked *, as shown in the first answer. The key is D major.

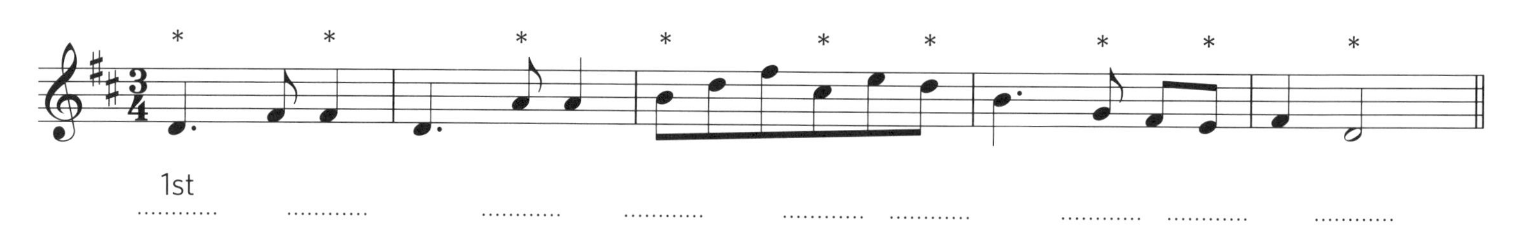

....

(b) How many semiquavers (16th notes) is the last note of the melody worth? ....

4 Name the key of each of these scales. Also draw a bracket (⌐¬) over each pair of notes making a semitone, as shown in the first scale.

10

Key ....

Key ....

Key ....

5 Answer **both** (a) and (b).

10

(a) Add the correct clef to each of these tonic triads.

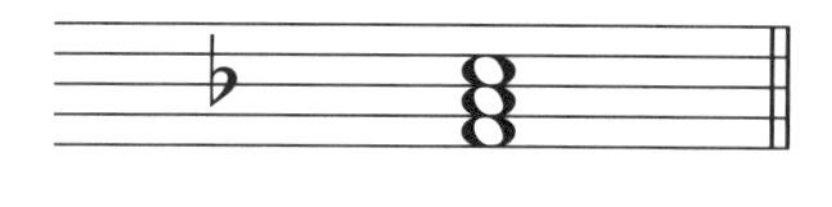

F major

D major

Letter names ....

(b) Under each triad write the letter name of each note, including the sharp sign where necessary.

6 **After** each note write a **higher** note to form the named **melodic** interval within the key of G major. The first answer is given.

10

4th

3rd

6th

7th

2nd

5th

7 Next to each rest write a note that has the same time value. The first answer is given.

10

8 Tick one box for each term/sign, as shown in the first answer.

10

crescendo means:

- gradually getting quieter ☐
- gradually getting louder ☑
- loud ☐
- quick ☐

mf means:

- quiet ☐
- very loud ☐
- moderately loud ☐
- moderately quiet ☐

rall. means:

- gradually getting slower ☐
- held back ☐
- slow ☐
- gradually getting quicker ☐

Allegro moderato means:

- moderately loud ☐
- moderately quiet ☐
- moderately slow ☐
- moderately quick ☐

(staccato note) means:

- *staccato*: smoothly ☐
- *staccato*: detached ☐
- accent the note ☐
- *legato*: detached ☐

dal segno (*D.S.*) means:

- repeat from the sign 𝄋 ☐
- the end ☐
- repeat from the beginning ☐
- in time ☐

9 Look at this melody and then answer the questions below.

Allegro ♩ = 100

rall.

f *ff*

Write your answer to question (b) on the stave below.

(a) (i) Give the number of a bar that contains **all** the notes of the tonic triad of D major. Bar ....

10

(ii) How many bars contain semiquavers (16th notes)? ....

(iii) Give the letter name of the **loudest** note in the melody. ....

(iv) Answer TRUE or FALSE to these sentences:

All the notes in bars 1–2 can be found in the key of D major. ....

The upper **4** in $\frac{4}{4}$ means the number of beats in a bar. ....

(b) Copy out the music from the start of bar 1 to the end of bar 2, exactly as it is written above. Don't forget the clef, key signature, time signature, tempo marking, dynamic and all other details. Write the music on the blank stave above question (a).

10

Theory Paper Grade 1 2019 S

Duration 1½ hours

TOTAL MARKS 100

Candidates should answer ALL questions.
Write your answers on this paper – no others will be accepted.
Answers must be written clearly and neatly – otherwise marks may be lost.

1 Add the missing bar-lines to these two melodies. The first bar-line is given in each.

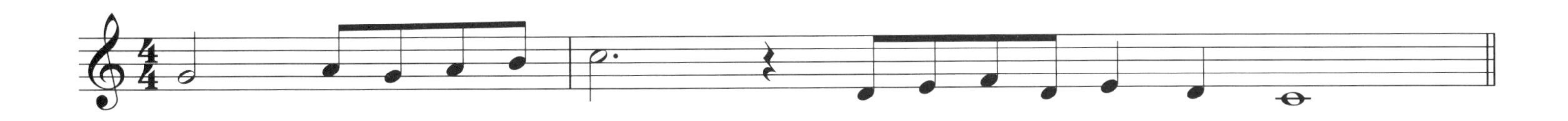

2 Add a rest at the places marked * in these two melodies to make each bar complete.

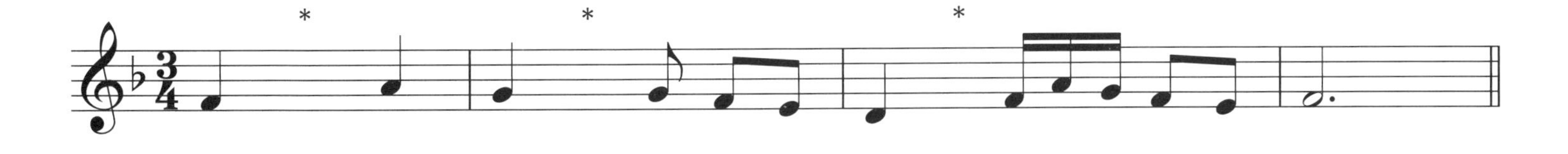

3 Answer **both** (a) and (b).

10

(a) Give the letter name of each of the notes marked *. The first answer is given.

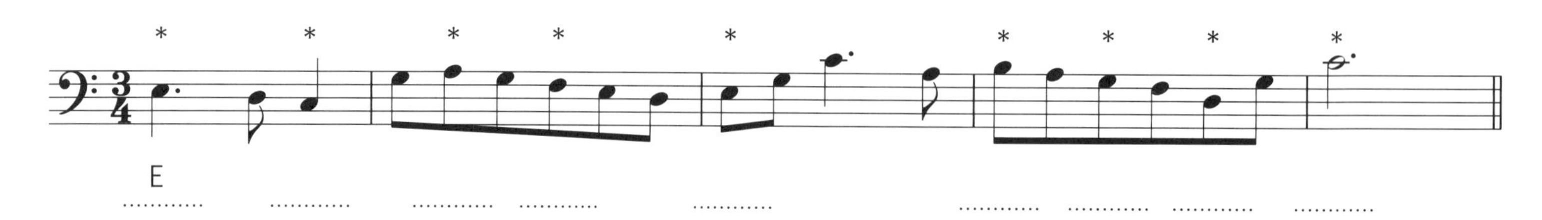

E

(b) How many bars contain a dotted crotchet (dotted quarter note)? ....

4 Add the correct clef and any necessary accidentals to make each of the scales named below. Do **not** use key signatures.

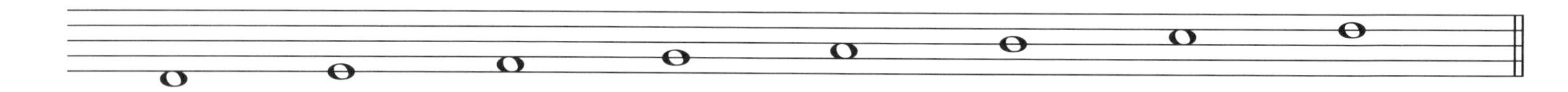

F major

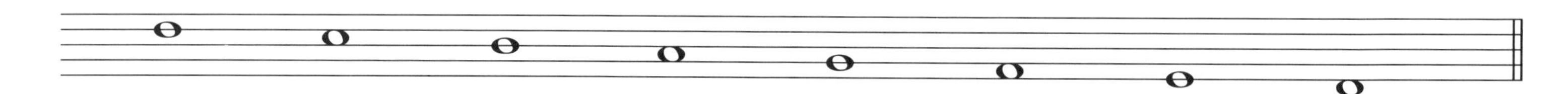

D major

5 Give the number (e.g. 2nd, 3rd) of each of these melodic intervals, as shown in the first answer. The key is G major.

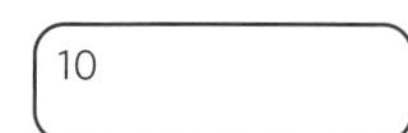

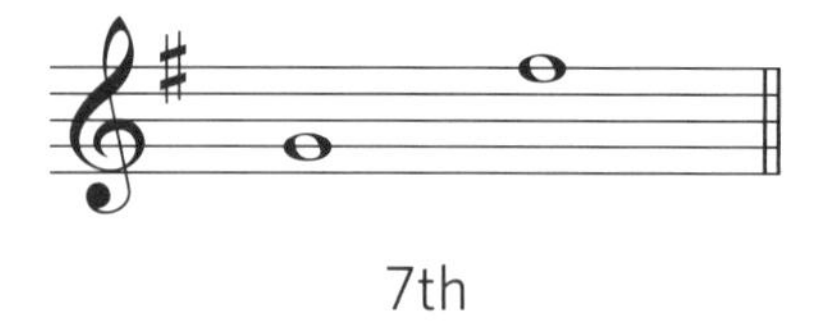

7th

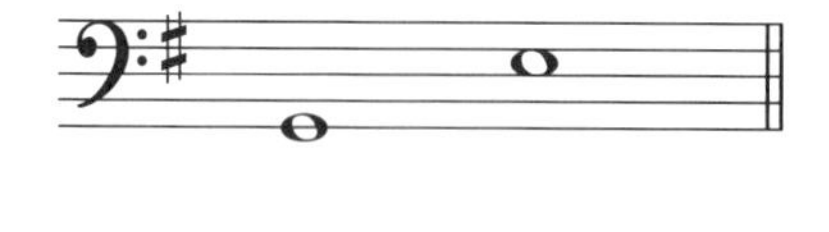

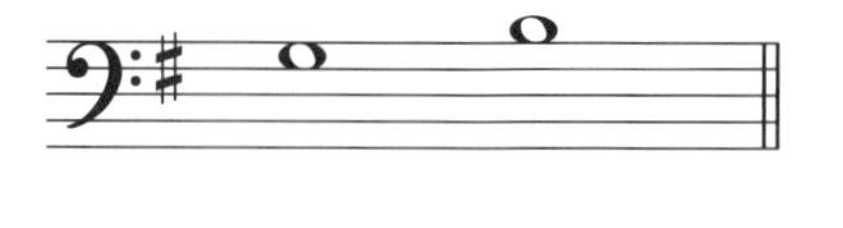

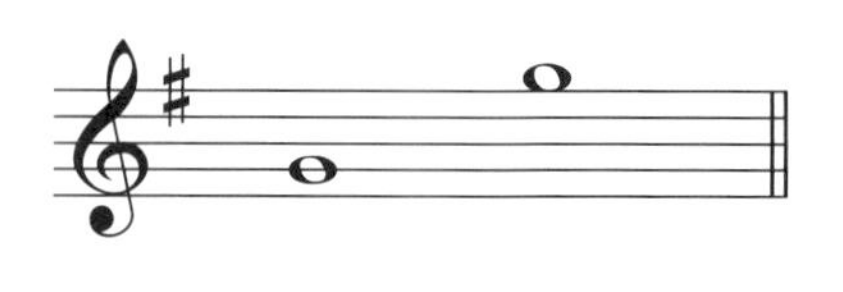

6 Name the major key of each of these tonic triads. The first answer is given. 10

G major

....

....

....

....

....

7 (a) Draw a circle around the **higher** note of each of these pairs of notes. 10

(b) Draw a circle around the **lower** note of each of these pairs of notes.

8 Tick one box for each term/sign, as shown in the first answer. 10

8va- - - - -˥ means:

- perform an octave lower ☐
- perform the notes smoothly ☐
- pause on the note or rest ☐
- perform an octave higher ☑

(accent on note) means:

- accent the note ☐
- *staccato*: detached ☐
- *staccato*: smoothly ☐
- *legato*: smoothly ☐

decrescendo means:

- gradually getting quieter ☐
- gradually getting slower ☐
- gradually getting quicker ☐
- quiet ☐

Allegretto means:

- slow ☐
- gradually getting quicker ☐
- fairly quick ☐
- gradually getting slower ☐

mp means:

- very quiet ☐
- moderately loud ☐
- moderately quick ☐
- moderately quiet ☐

staccato means:

- smoothly ☐
- detached ☐
- accent ☐
- loud ☐

9 Look at this melody and then answer the questions below.

Write your answer to question (b) on the stave below.

(a) (i) Give the time name (e.g. crotchet or quarter note) of the **shortest** note in the melody. ....

10

(ii) In which bar is the player told to pause or hold on to a note? Bar ....

(iii) The melody is in the key of G major. Name the degree of the scale (e.g. 2nd, 3rd) of the first note in bar 4 (marked ↓). ....

(iv) Give the number of a bar that contains **all** the notes of the tonic triad of G major. Bar ....

(v) Answer TRUE or FALSE to this sentence:

The **4** in $\frac{3}{4}$ means crotchet (quarter note) beats. ....

(b) Copy out the music from the start of bar 1 to the end of bar 4, exactly as it is written above. Don't forget the clef, key signature, time signature, tempo marking, dynamics and all other details. Write the music on the blank stave above question (a).

10